Delightful Handwriting

Zaner Bloser Copybook

by
Lanaya Gore

Delightful Handwriting Zaner Bloser Copybook
Text © 2011, Lanaya Gore

Cover Design: John Shafer
Cover Art: Jessie Willcox Smith

ISBN 978-1-61634-138-1 (printed book)
ISBN 978-1-61634-139-8 (e-book)

Published and printed by
Simply Charlotte Mason, LLC
P. O. Box 892
Grayson, Georgia 30017-0892

SimplyCharlotteMason.com

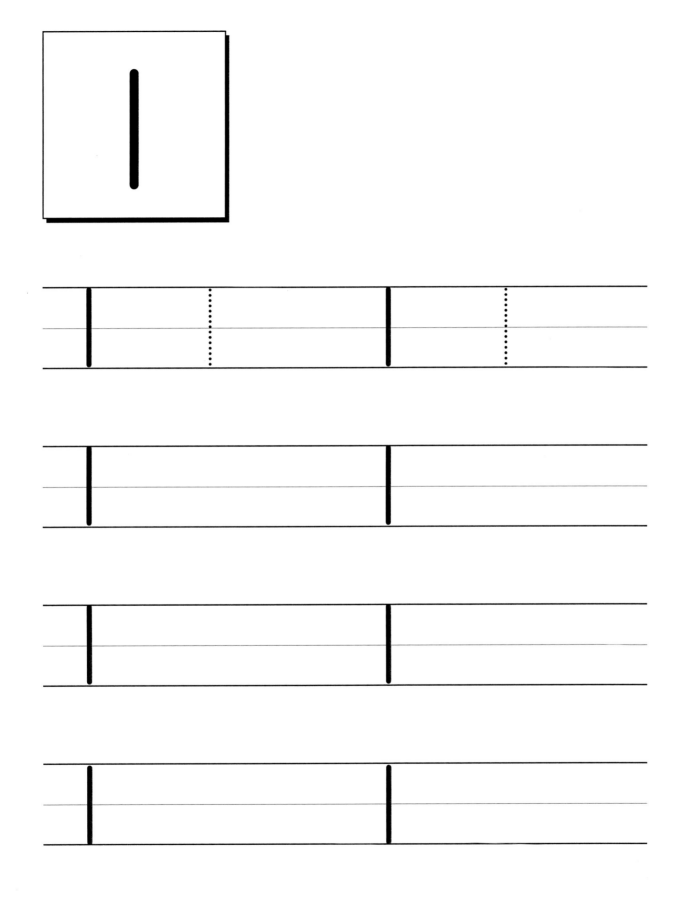

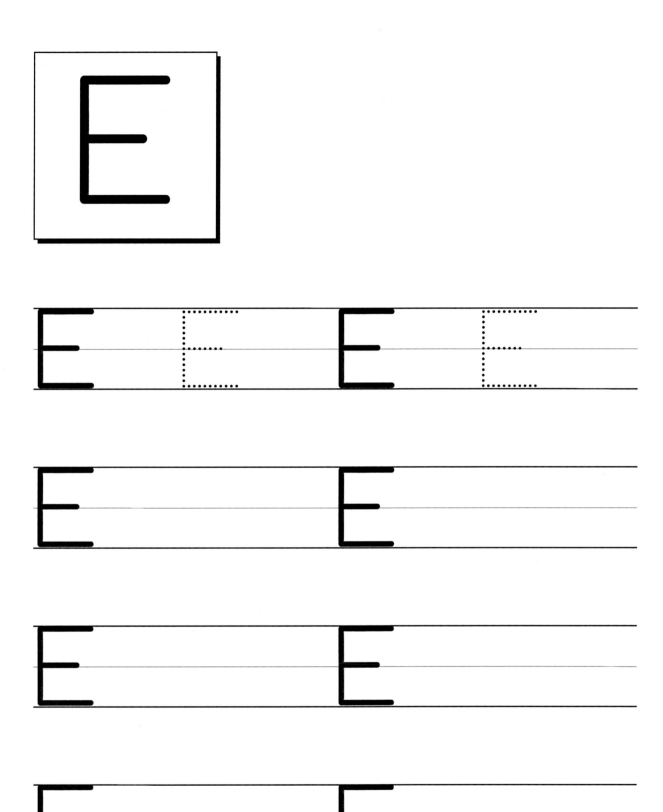

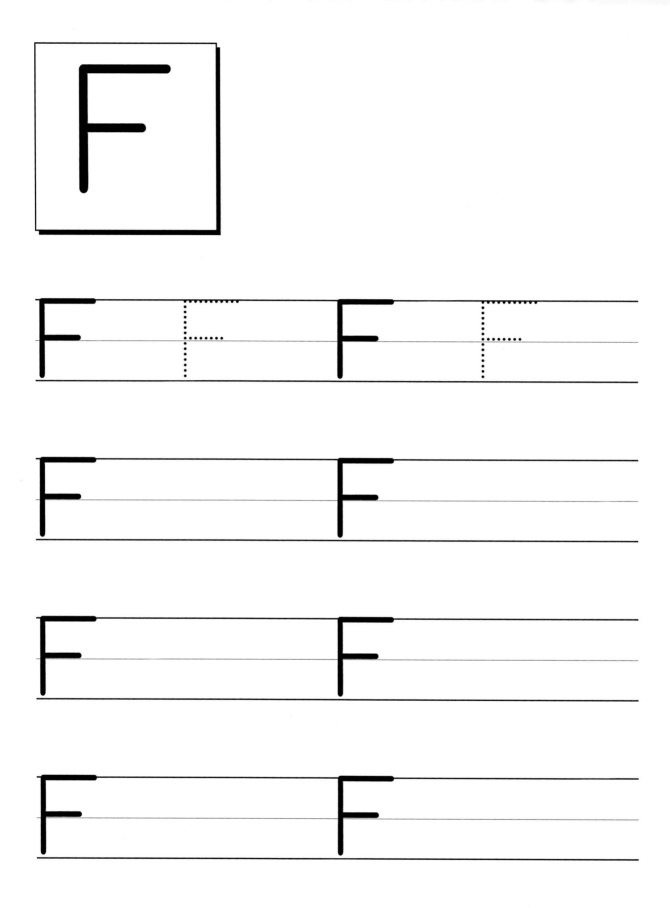

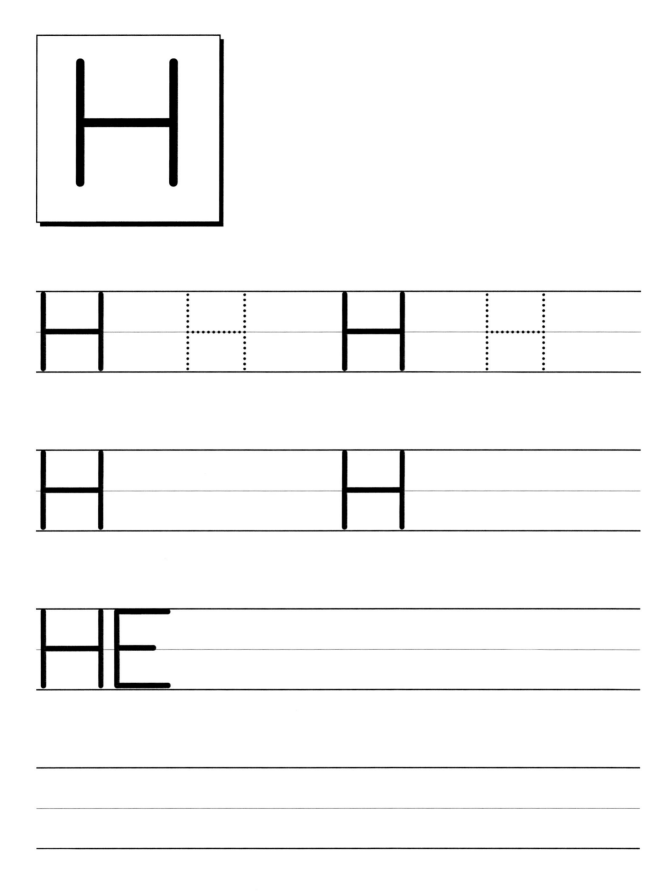

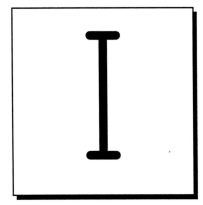

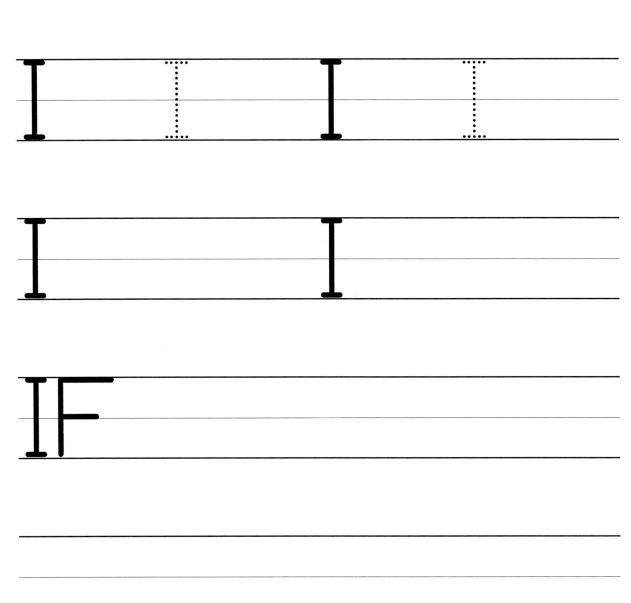

HI

FEE

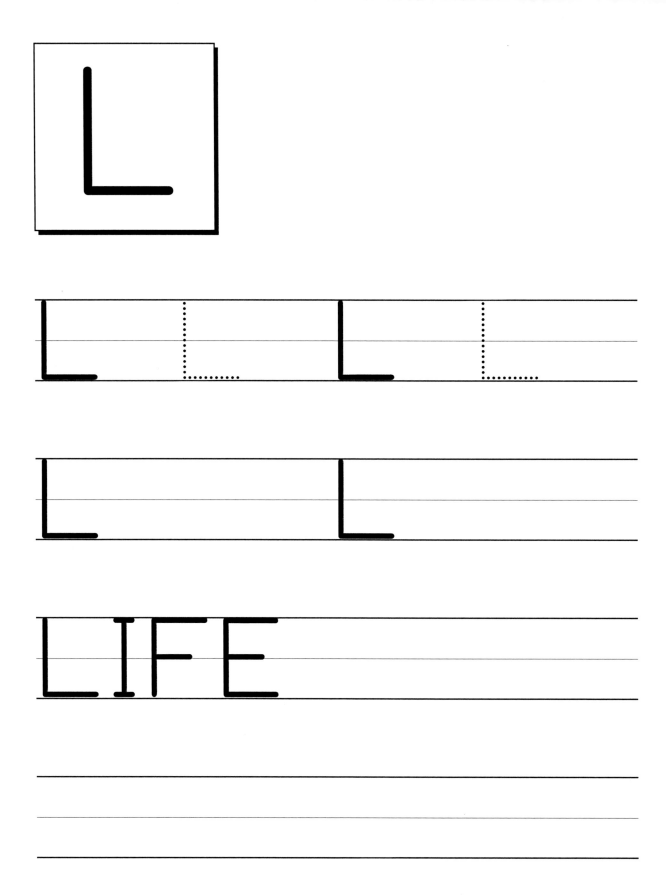

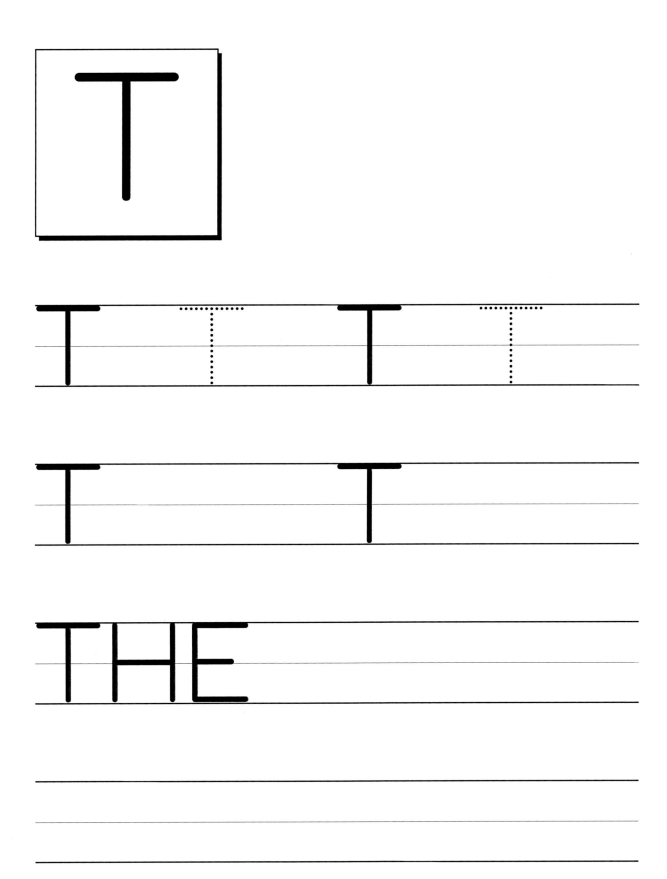

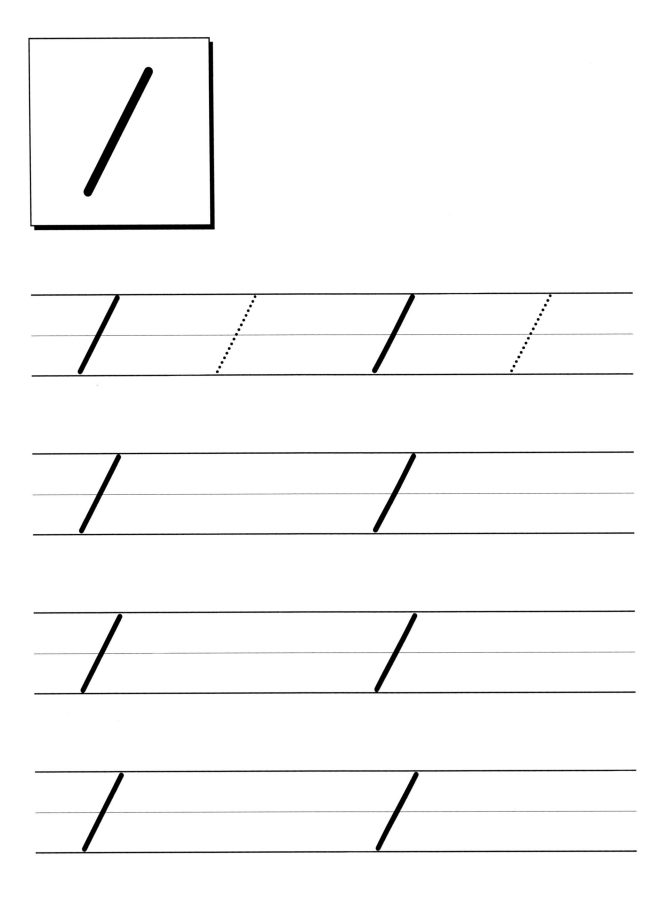

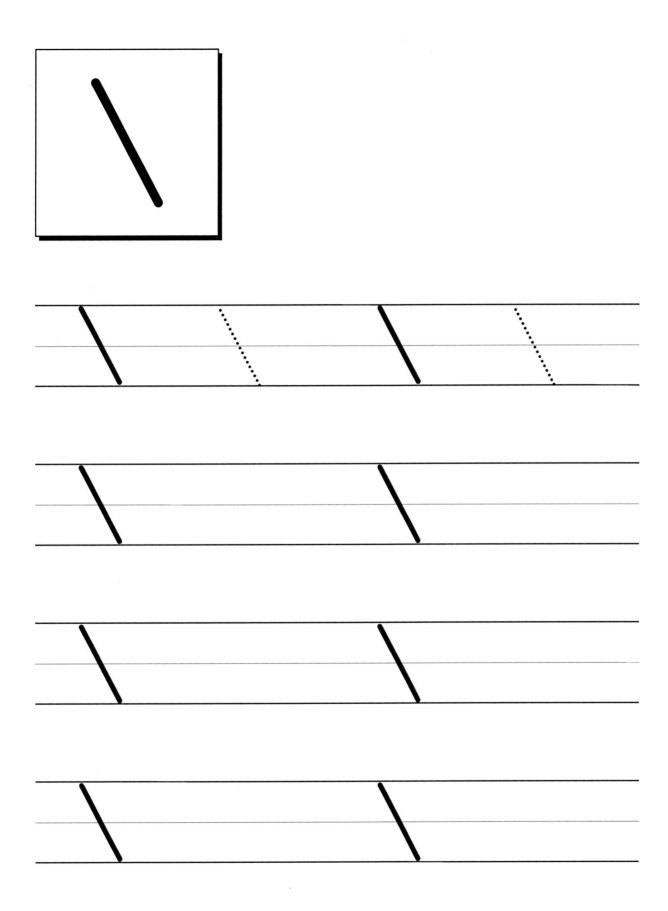

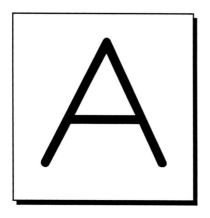

A A A A A

A A

ALL

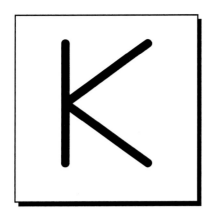

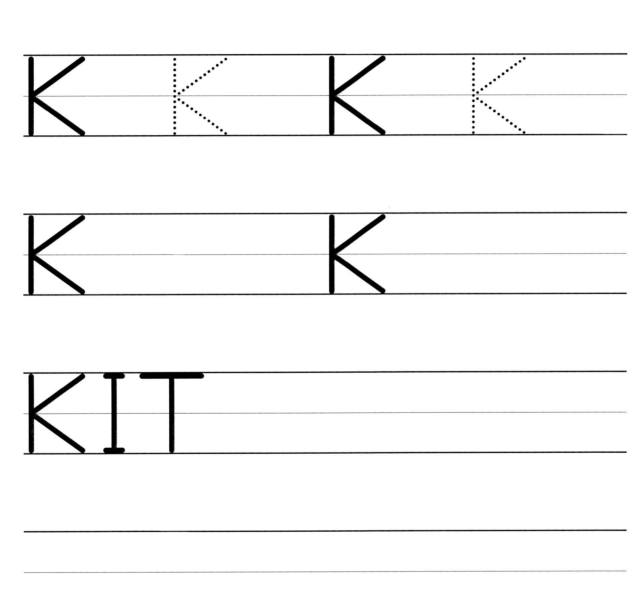

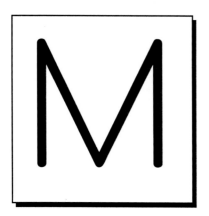

M M M M M

M M

MAT

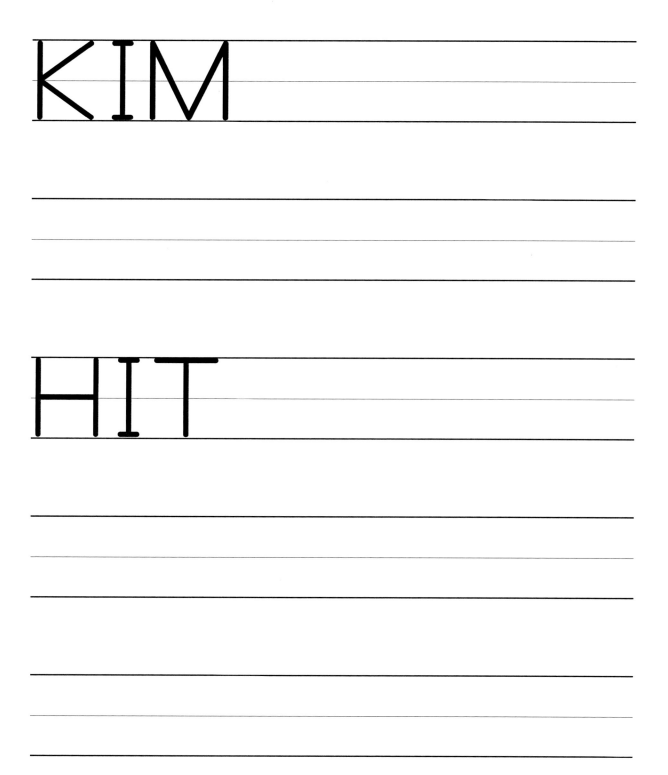

KIM

HIT

FLEA

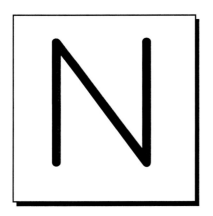

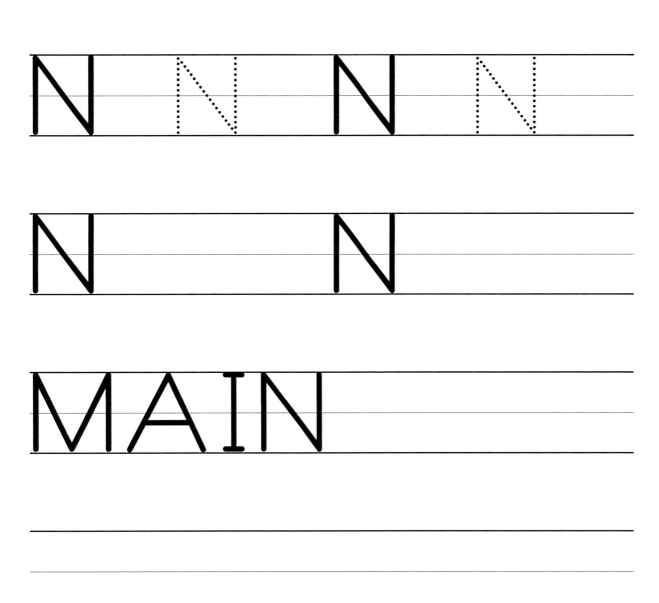

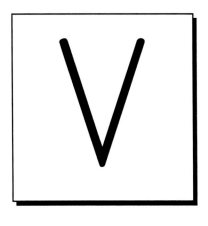

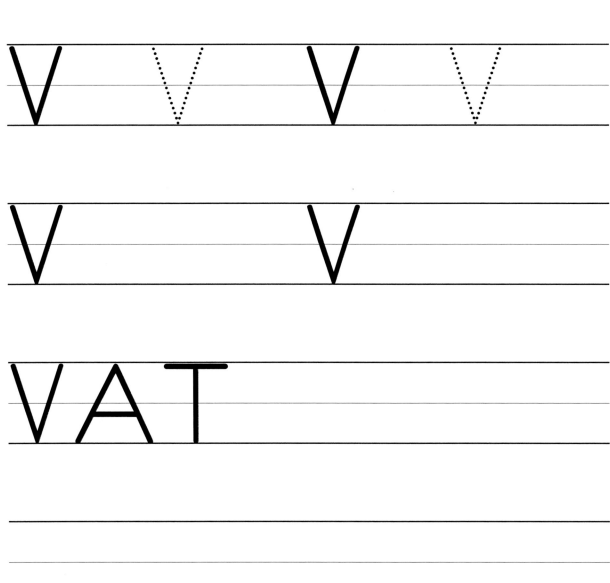

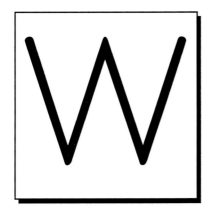

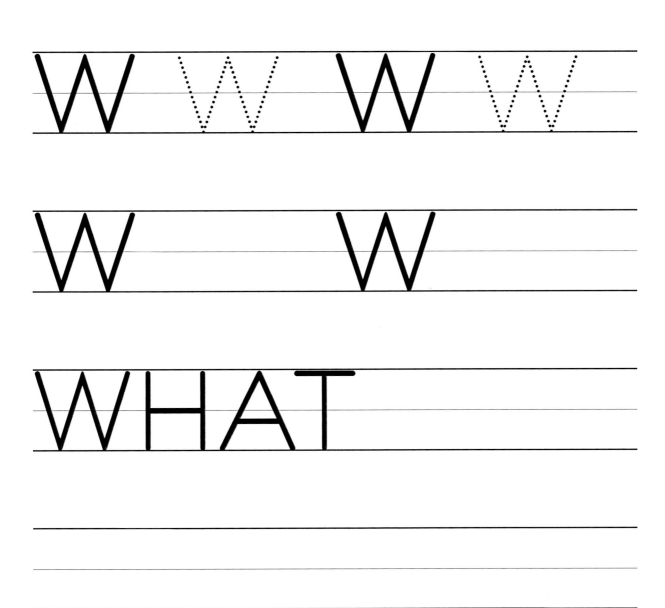

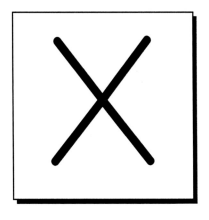

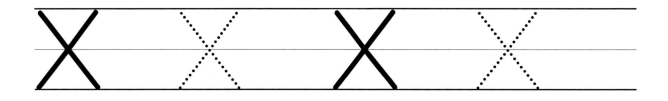

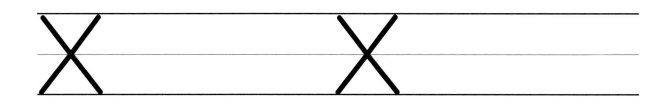

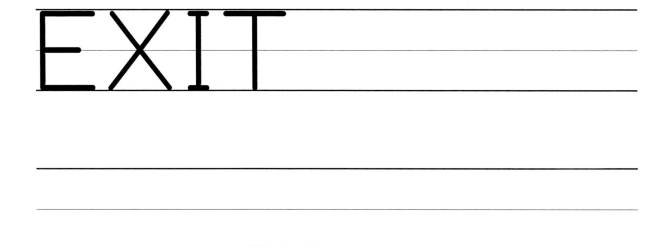

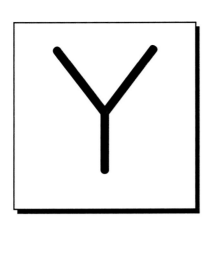

YEA

Z

Z Z Z Z Z

Z   Z

ZANY

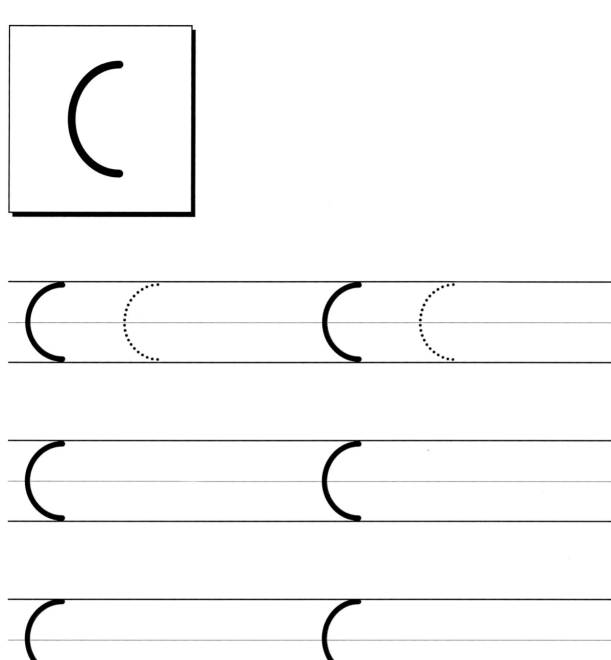

WIT

YE

VAIN

ZAZZY

NEXT

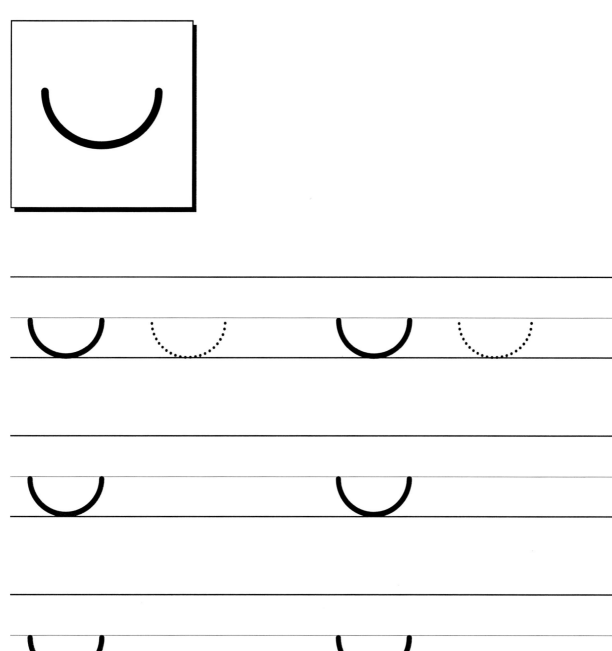

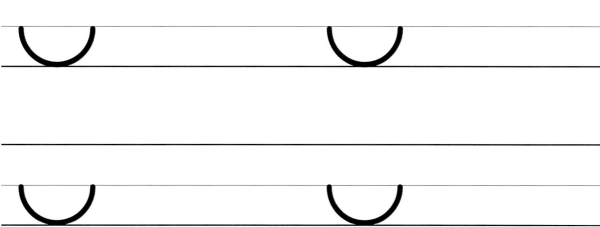

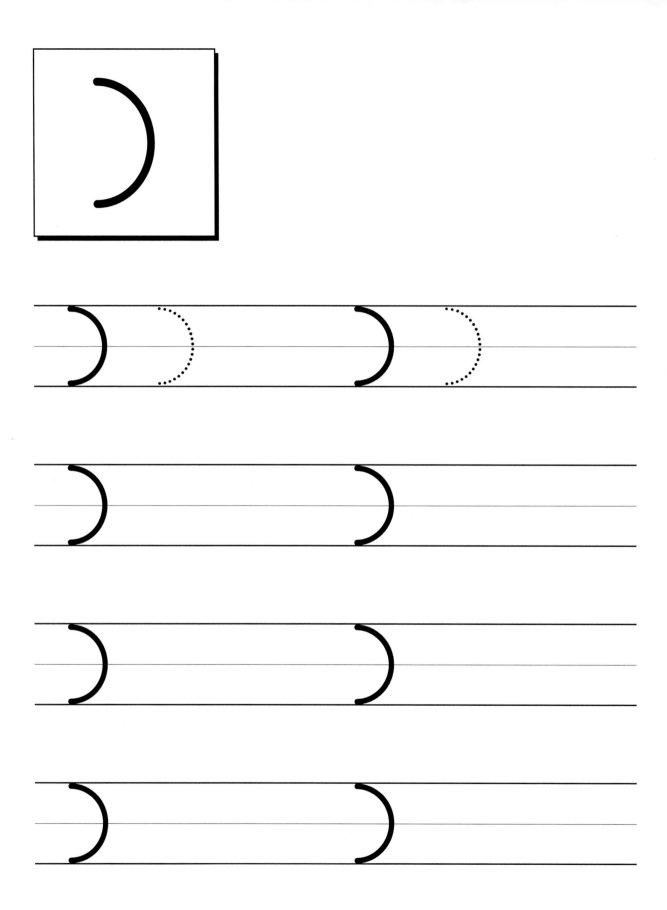

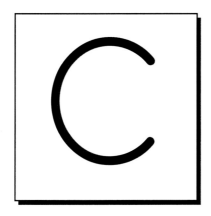

C   C   C   C   C

C   C

CHAT

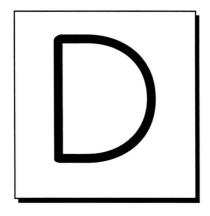

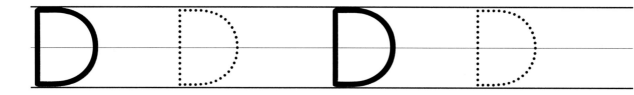

D   D

WIELD

G

G G G G

G G

AGAIN

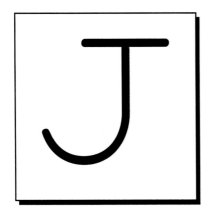

J J J J J

J   J

JACK

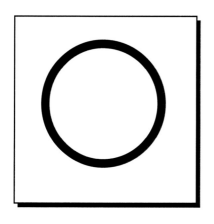

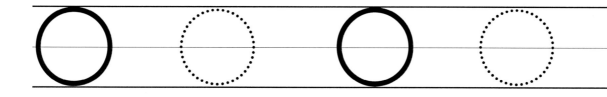

WON

CAT

JON

GLAND

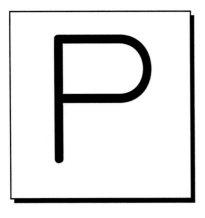

P P P P

P P

DIP

R

R R R R

R R

MERE

_____

_____

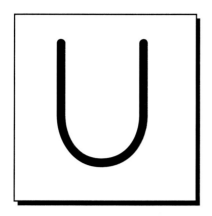

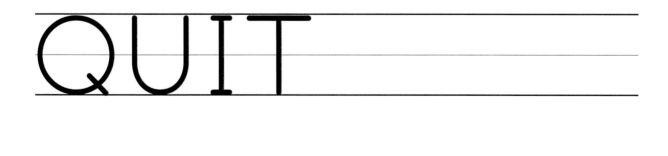

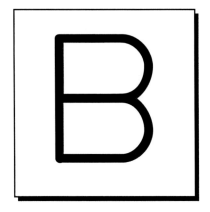

B B B B

B B

BOUND

S

S   S   S   S

S   S

SKIPS

QUIPS

BRAND

MY

NAME

IS

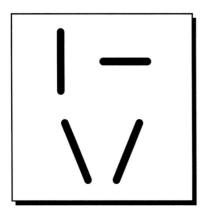

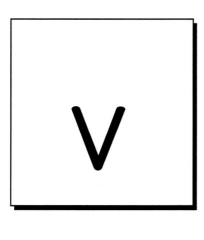

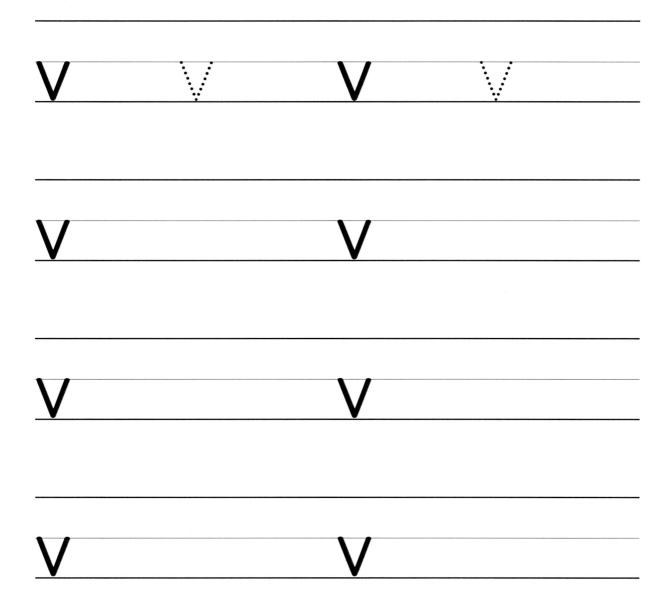

Z

z   z   z   z

z   z

z   z

z   z

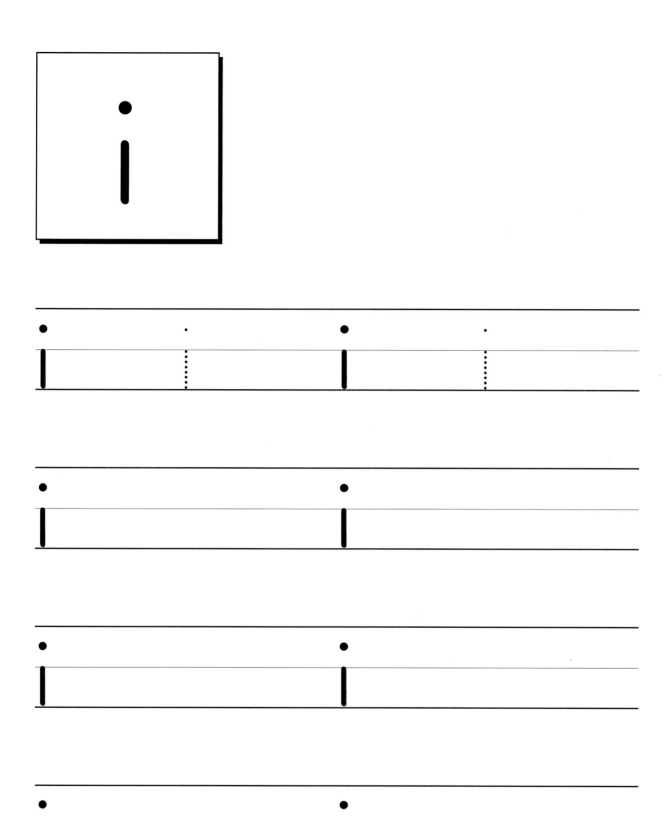

i

v

Z

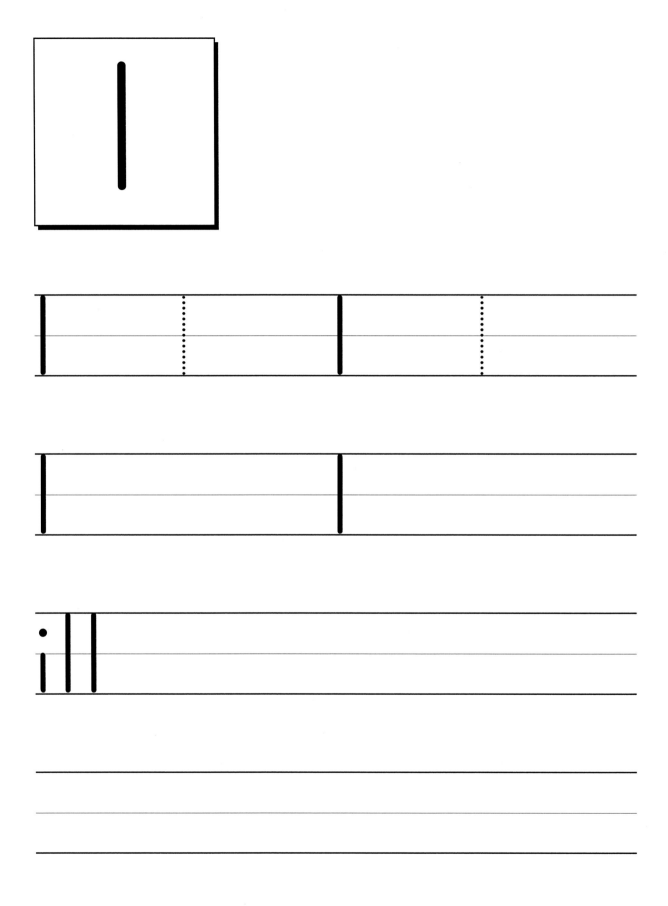

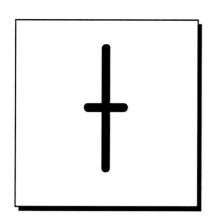

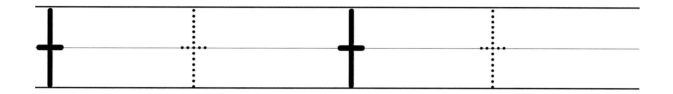

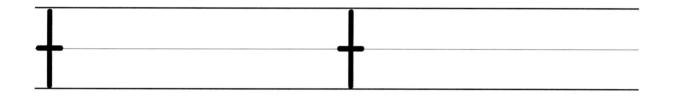

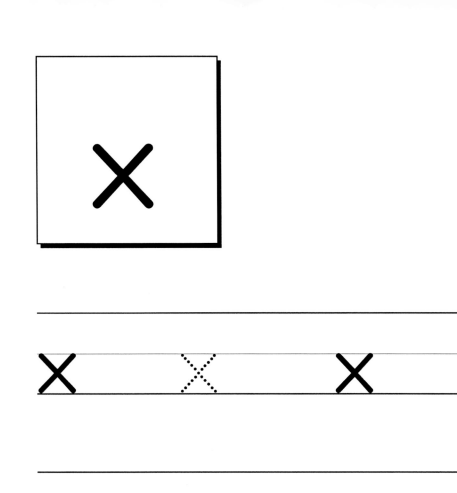

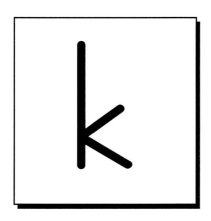

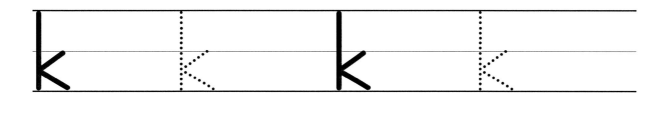

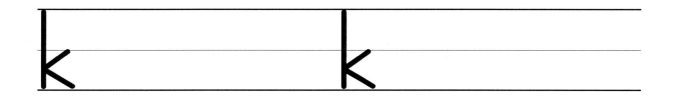

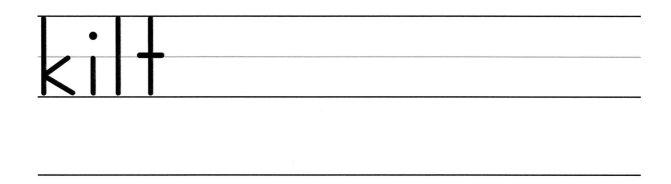

kilt

kit

Liz

x

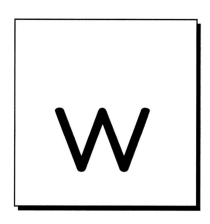

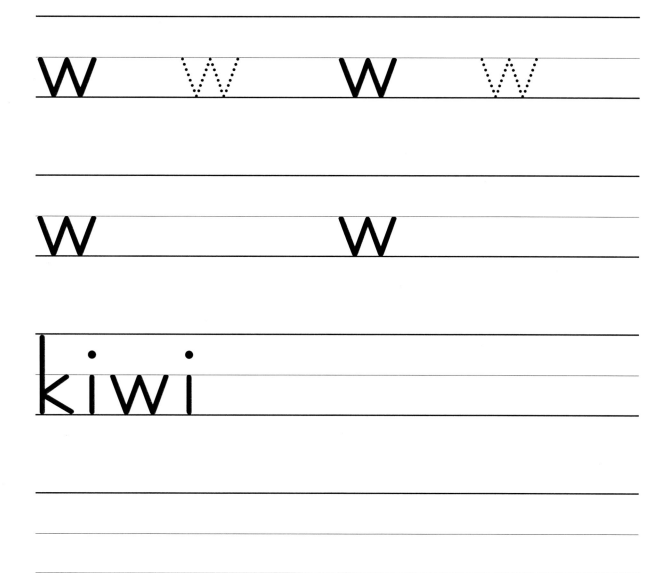

W   W   W   W

W   W

kiwi

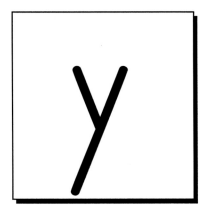

y   y   y   y

y   y

xyz

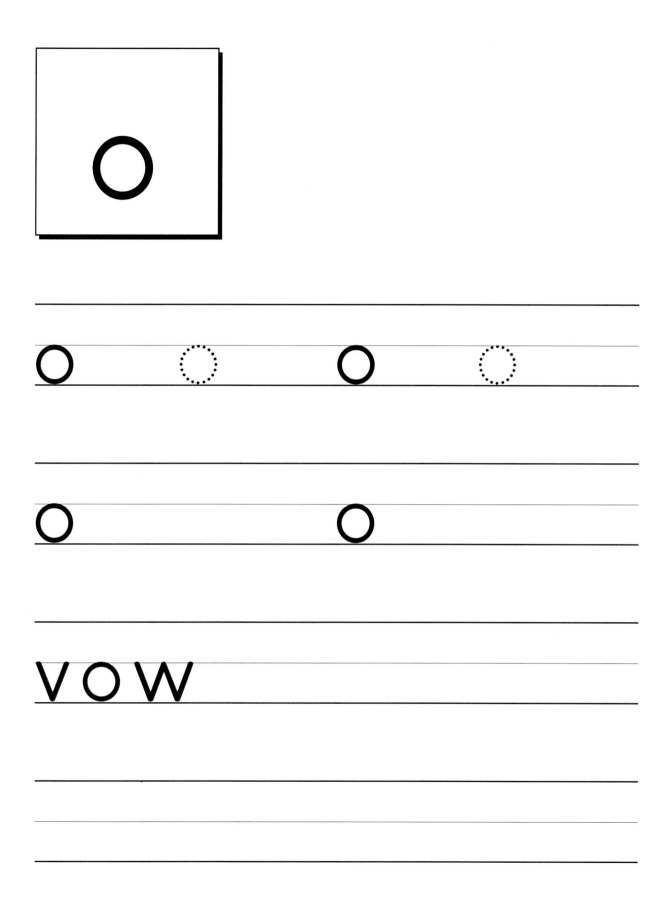

VOW

a

a   a   a   a

a   a

law

tot

yay

WOW

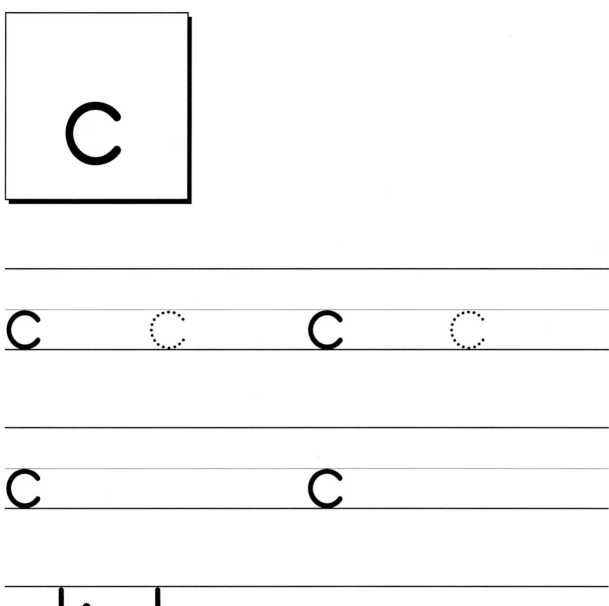

c   c   c   c

c   c

click

g

g   g   g   g

g   g

go

e

e   e   e   e

e   e

alive

s

s   s   s   s

s   s

last

cast

eagle

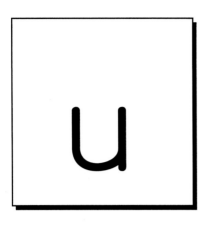

u   u

you

q

q q q q

q q

quick

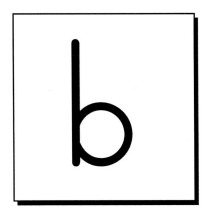

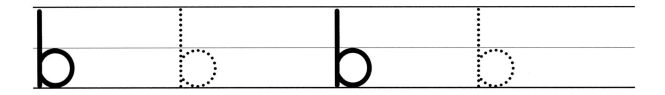

b   b

box

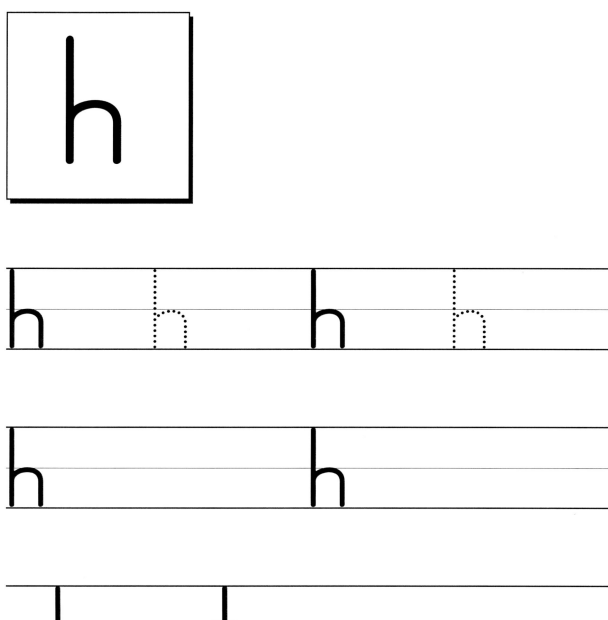

shout

quill

shut

bog

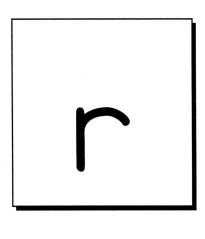

r r r r

r r

hear

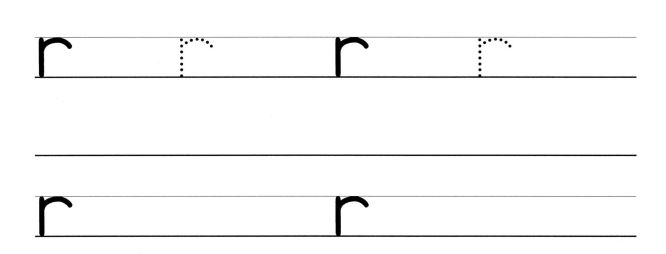

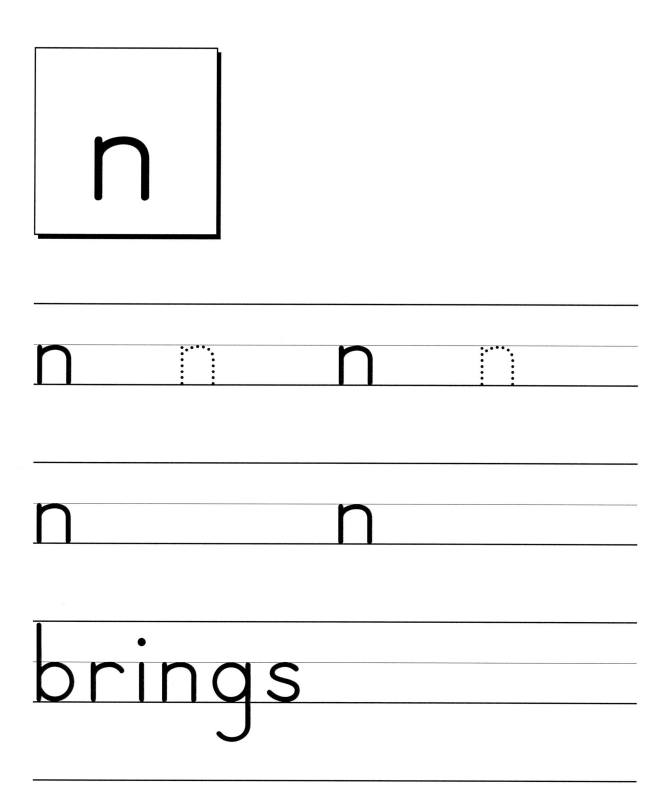

n

n   n   n   n

n   n

brings

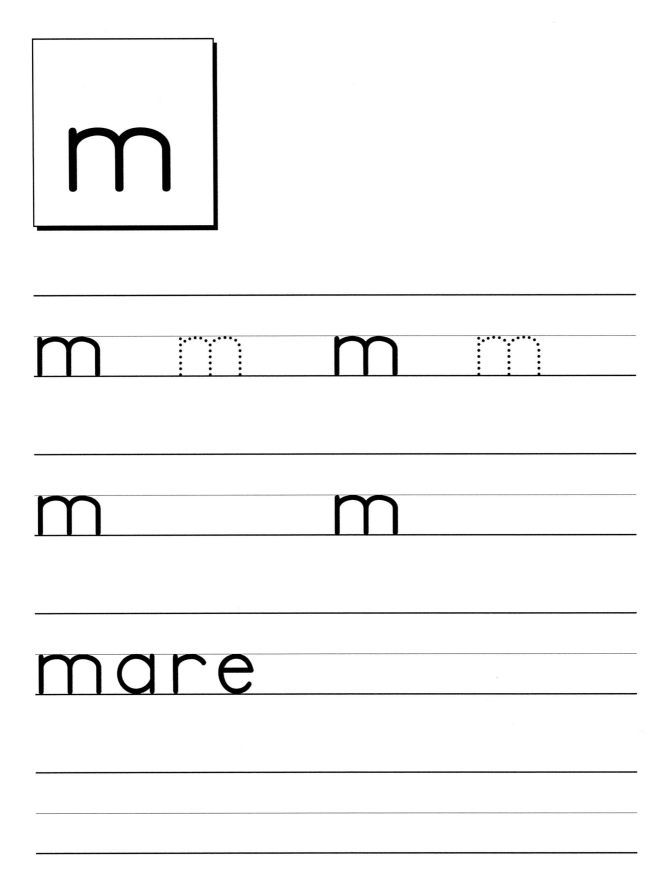

m m m m m

m m

mare

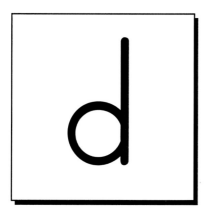

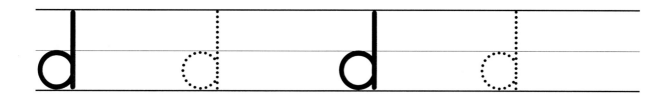

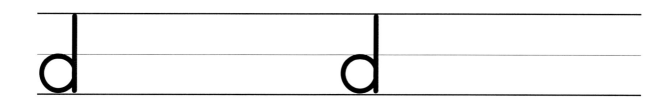

grind

skin

dry

home

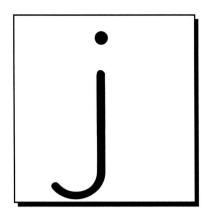

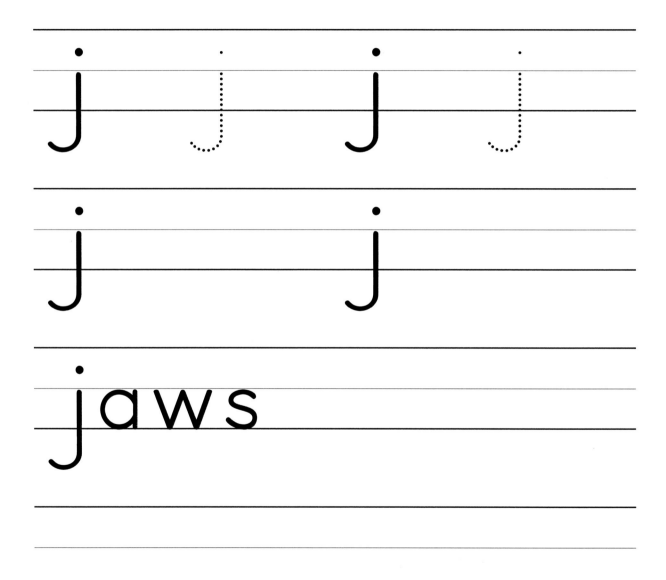

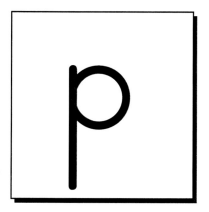

p   p   p   p

p   p

paint

doff

phone

finding

jet

The rain

is falling

all around,

It falls

on field

and tree,

It rains

on the

umbrellas

here,

And on the

ships at sea.

Some dogs,

finding the

skin of a lion

began to

tear it in

pieces with

their teeth.

A fox,

seeing them,

said: "If this

lion were

alive, you

would soon

find out

that his

claws were

stronger than

your teeth."

Moral: It is
easy to kick
a man that

is down.

Do not wear

yourself out to

get rich; have

the wisdom to

show restraint.

Cast but a

glance at

riches, and they

are gone,

for they will

surely sprout

wings and fly

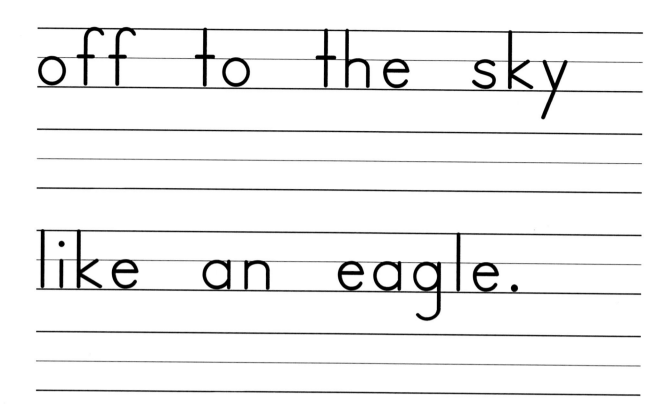

off to the sky

like an eagle.

Aa Bb Cc Dd

Ee Ff Gg Hh

Ii Jj Kk Ll

Mm Nn Oo Pp

Qq Rr Ss Tt

Uu Vv Ww Xx

Yy Zz